Sophie

PINAFORE

H.M.S. PINAFORE

STORY AND MUSIC ARRANGEMENTS
ADAPTED FROM GILBERT AND SULLIVAN BY

OPAL WHEELER

ILLUSTRATED BY **FRITZ KREDEL**

E.P. DUTTON AND CO., INC. NEW YORK 1946

S. A. JACOBS, THE GOLDEN EAGLE PRESS
MOUNT VERNON, N.Y.

FOR

Pamela, Jill, and Jack

MUSICAL SELECTIONS

PINAFORE

PART ONE

THE old harbor of Portsmouth glowed like a deep blue jewel in the clear dawn, clouds of hungry gulls flashing over its shining waters and plummeting suddenly below for a good catch of fresh juicy fish for a tasty breakfast.

Out of the mighty sea charged the sun, and there, riding jauntily at anchor in a blaze of golden light lay Her Majesty's Ship, the PINAFORE, every loyal seaman aboard the old scarred man-o'-war up and stirring on this special day of all the year.

Shouts of command, bits of songs and gay laughter rang merrily over the sun flecked water as decks were swabbed and every nook and corner turned inside out for a good sound scrubbing.

There was no time to lose, for the celebrated Sir Joseph Porter, First Lord of the Admiralty and Knight Commander of the Bath, would be coming this very day for his yearly visit to the famed old guard ship.

"Shine her up, mates!" called the boatswain, proudly, "And we'll show the Admiral the sauciest little ship ever to sail in the British Navy!"

"Aye, aye, sir!" came the hearty reply, as with fresh vigor the cleaning and polishing went on until the brasses began to shine like molten gold for the close inspection of the royal master of the seas.

"And there'll be more than inspection, maties," said a brawny tar, hard at work splicing old rope, "They say that Sir Joseph seeks the hand of our Captain's daughter."

"The fair Josephine?"

"None other!"

There was still much to be done, and as all hands worked happily away, their rousing song of the sea rang out lustily on the swiftly mounting tide.

We Sail the Ocean Blue

We — sail the o-cean blue, And our sau-cy ship's a beau-ty

We're— so-ber men and true, And at-ten-tive to our du-ty

When the balls whis-tle free O'er the bright blue sea, We stand to our

guns all _ day; _ When at an-chor we ride on the Ports-mouth

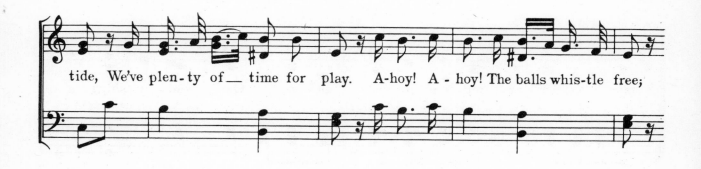

tide, We've plen-ty of_ time for play. A-hoy! A-hoy! The balls whis-tle free;

A-hoy! A-hoy! O'er the bright blue_ sea, We stand to our guns,

To our guns all day, _____ We_ sail the o-cean

blue, And our sau - cy ship's a beau - ty, We're— so - ber men and

true And at - ten - tive to our du - ty. Our sau - cy ship's a

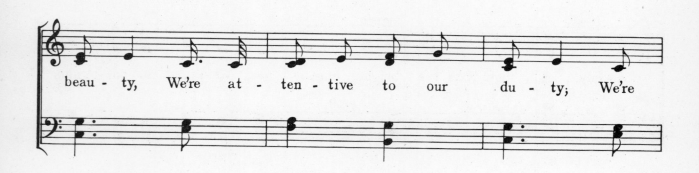

beau - ty, We're at - ten - tive to our du - ty; We're

sob - er men and true, We sail the o - - cean blue.

As the last merry strains rang out over the busy decks, who should come bouncing over the ship's side but the plump, smiling peddler woman, friend of all the sailors, called Little Buttercup by her good customers these many years.

Over her arm, her heavy basket was as temptingly laden as ever.

"Hail, man-o'-war's men!" she called gaily, "Now that you have your pay, spare all you can to welcome your Little Buttercup."

With a shout the men crowded around the buxom Mrs. Cripps, delving into her basket and exploring it to the bottom.

"Peppermint drops!" cried a slender tar, popping three or four into his watering mouth.

"Tobaccy!" called another merrily, hurrying off to fill his pipe.

"I'll have this fine watch."

"See, Buttercup, this knife is for me."

"Now the lace will do for my sweet young wife."

"And that fat hen will keep us all from hunger."

Little Buttercup laughed heartily at the scrambling sailors, rescuing what little was left at the bottom of her basket.

Around the deck she bowed to her admiring audience, entertaining her good customers with a song that they liked so well to hear: "I'm called Little Buttercup, dear Little Buttercup, though I could never tell why."

I'm Called Little Buttercup*

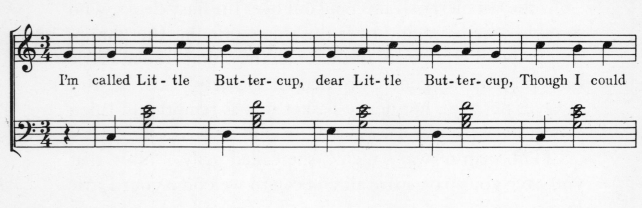

I'm called Lit - tle But - ter - cup, dear Lit - tle But - ter - cup, Though I could

nev - er tell why, — — But still I'm called But - ter - cup,

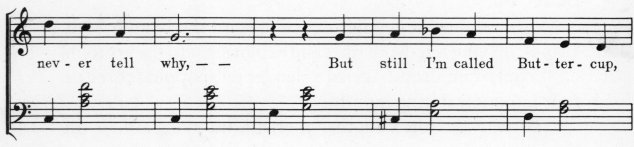

poor Lit - tle But - ter - cup, Sweet Lit - tle But - ter - cup I, — — I've

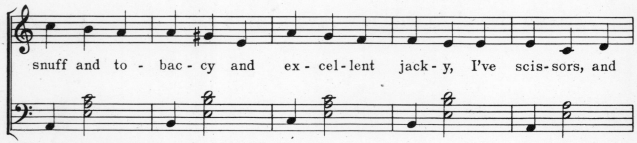

snuff and to - bac - cy and ex - cel - lent jack - y, I've scis - sors, and

*The melody of this song may be played in octaves.

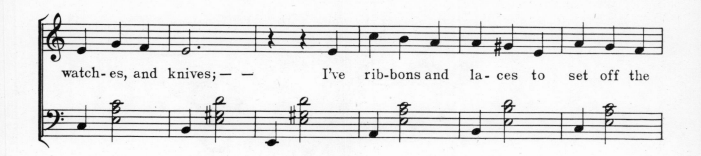

watch- es, and knives; — — I've rib-bons and la- ces to set off the

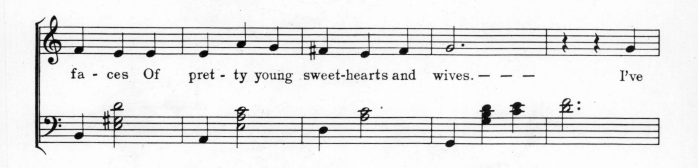

fa - ces Of pret - ty young sweet-hearts and wives. — — — I've

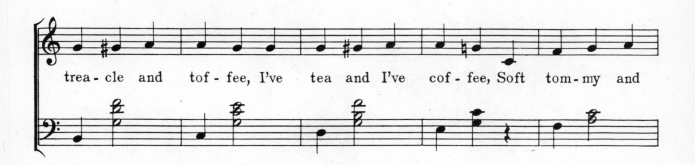

trea - cle and tof - fee, I've tea and I've cof - fee, Soft tom- my and

suc - cu-lent chops; — — I've chick-ens and co-nies, and pret - ty po-

lo - nies, And ex - cel - lent pep - per - mint drops, _____ Then

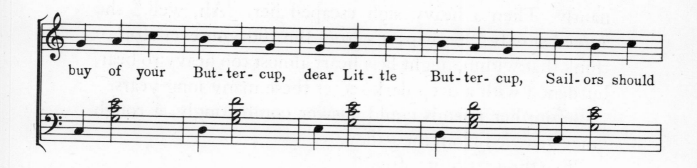

buy of your But - ter - cup, dear Lit - tle But - ter - cup, Sail - ors should

nev - er be shy; — — — So buy of your But - ter - cup,

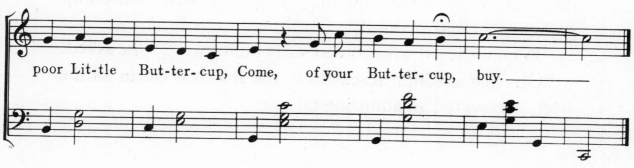

poor Lit - tle But - ter - cup, Come, of your But - ter - cup, buy. _____

Cheers rang full-throated from the delighted sailor lads.

"Buttercup! Buttercup! Hail, Little Buttercup!"

"Aye, Little Buttercup, and well named," called the boatswain, "for you're the rosiest, the roundest, and the reddest beauty in all Spithead."

But Buttercup was not at all pleased with his words.

"Red am I, and round, and rosy!" she exclaimed indignantly. Then a heavy sigh escaped her. "Ah, well," she agreed slowly, "perhaps it's true. But did you ever stop to think that within, might lie a heart almost too heavy to bear, burdened with a deep dark secret these many long years?"

Before her friends could answer comfortingly, a rough voice growled from the galley.

"I've thought of it, often!"

Buttercup drew back in horror at sight of the gruesome tar with criss-cross patch drawn over one eye.

"Don't take notice of him; that's only poor Dick Deadeye," explained one of the sailors quickly.

"The twisted, sour-faced tar shuffled closer.

"Yes, that's it — I'm Dick Deadeye," he muttered. "Its a beastly name, ain't it, Buttercup?"

Her answer came slowly. "It isn't a very pretty name."

At that very moment there appeared in the hatchway a tall, handsome sailor, moving so slowly that Buttercup looked after him anxiously.

"Who is the lad who goes so sadly on his way?" she asked.

"Oh, that is Ralph Rackstraw, the smartest lad in all the fleet," answered an admiring tar.

At the very sound of the words, Buttercup turned pale, and wheeling suddenly, she rushed away murmuring, "That name! That name! Ah, woe is me!"

It was all too true. Ralph loved Josephine dearly, but alas, she was far above the station of a simple British tar. As he sang his song of love, the sailors gathered around him quietly, listening as the sad words poured from his heart:

'Oh pity, pity me; Our Captain's daughter she,
   And I, that lowly suitor.'

"Poor lad," sighed the boatswain when the song had died away, "you've climbed too high. Our Captain's daughter will have nothing to say to you."

"No!" shouted Dick Deadeye fiercely. "Captain's daughters don't marry foremast hands!"

Instantly the men were on their feet, ready to punish this shameful outburst, when suddenly before them appeared the Captain. In a flash, every tar was at cheerful attention.

"My gallant crew, good morning," greeted Captain Corcoran briskly. "I hope you are quite well."

"Quite well, sir," came the hearty reply.

Breaking into merry song, the warm hearted Captain told his crew how well he thought of them and their powers on the water and what he, himself, could do on shipboard, adding that in the very fiercest gales, he was never, never sick at sea.

Well, *hardly* ever!

I Am the Captain of the Pinafore

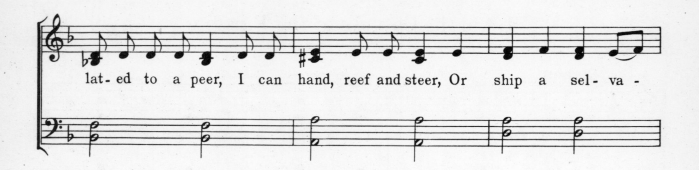

lat- ed to a peer, I can hand, reef and steer, Or ship a sel - va -

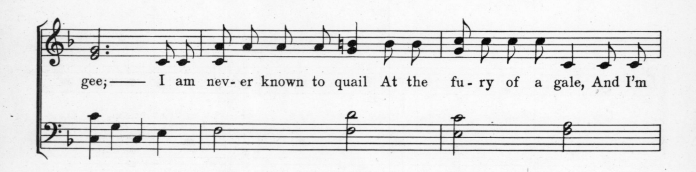

gee;——— I am nev- er known to quail At the fu - ry of a gale, And I'm

SAILORS   CAPTAIN   SAILORS

nev- er, nev- er sick at sea!——What, nev- er? No, nev- er! What,

CAPTAIN   SAILORS

nev - er? Well, hard-ly ev - er! He's hard-ly ev - er sick at

24

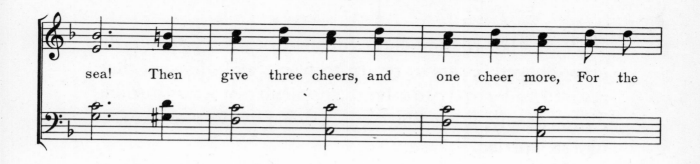

sea! Then give three cheers, and one cheer more, For the

hard-y cap-tain of the Pin-a-fore! Then give three cheers, and

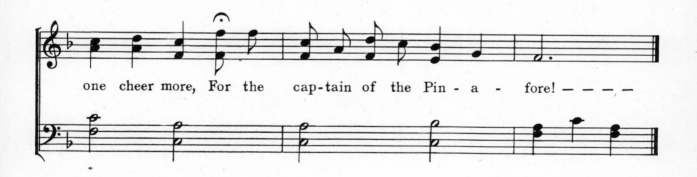

one cheer more, For the cap-tain of the Pin-a-fore! ———— —

With a last rousing cheer for their beloved Captain, the crew obeyed orders to return to work, and off went their revered leader to try to solve the problem that was disturbing him so deeply. Little Buttercup, passing by, was upset to see him so worried.

"Ah, Captain, your heart is heavy," she cried. "Tell me what is wrong."

"Much is wrong, Little Buttercup. My daughter Josephine, the fairest flower in all the world, is sought in marriage by none other than the great Sir Joseph Porter. But alas, she does not take kindly to him."

"Good Captain, have no fears, I pray you," comforted Mrs. Cripps. "Your problems will all be solved."

At that very moment the beautiful and gracious Josephine, her heart heavy within her, came slowly from her cabin, singing of her sadness to the sea:

"Sorry her lot who loves too well;
Heavy the heart that hopes but vainly."

"Ah, my child," cried Captain Corcoran, "it grieves me to see you so disconsolate. And you should be looking your best, with Sir Joseph coming this very day to claim your promised hand."

At the very mention of his name, Josephine cried out in alarm.

"But my heart is already given!"

"Given!" exclaimed the Captain. "And to whom?"

Josephine's head bent low and her words came slowly.

"Oh pity me, Father — he is a humble sailor aboard your own ship."

"A common sailor!" cried the Captain in despair. "Come, come, my child — this cannot be. The daughter of a Captain could never marry one so far beneath her station."

Now Josephine was proud, and at these words from her father, her head was slowly lifted.

"Very well," said she quietly, "I will obey your wishes. And though I carry my love with me forever, he shall never know."

Suddenly over the ship's side came the sound of singing.

"See, my child, Sir Joseph's barge is approaching, manned by twelve trusty oarsmen," exclaimed the Captain. "And there, accompanying him, are his admiring sisters, cousins, and aunts."

With ribbons and laces flying, the merry maidens danced aboard ship, followed by the pompous Sir Joseph and his favorite cousin, Hebe. From the bridge, Captain Corcoran led the way in a rousing cheer.

"Hooray! Hooray! Hooray!" echoed mightily over the ship.

Short, plump Sir Joseph, in tight fitting uniform covered with gleaming gold braid and fine plumed hat sitting jauntily on his round head, took his stand before the company.

Now Sir Joseph knew nothing about the sea. In fact, he had never even been at sea, but straightening himself proudly, and giving a twirl to his waxed moustaches, he put his monocle to his left eye, and in loud tones, told how he was the noted Monarch of the Sea.

I Am the Monarch of the Sea

SIR JOSEPH

I am the mon-arch of the sea,—— The rul-er of the Queen's Na-vee,——

SISTERS, COUSINS, AUNTS

Whose praise Great Brit-ain loud-ly chants: And we are his sis-ters and his

cous-ins and his aunt's! And we are his sis-ters and his

cous-ins and his aunts, His sis-ters and his cous-ins and his aunts!—-—

I gen-er-al-ly go be-low,—— And seek the se-clu-sion that a ca-bin grants!

SISTERS, COUSINS, AUNTS

And so do his sis-ters and his cous-ins and his aunts,

And so do his sis-ters and his cous-ins and his aunts,

And so do his sis-ters and his cous-ins and his aunts,

His sis-ters and his cous-ins, Whom he reck-ons up by doz-ens, and his aunts!

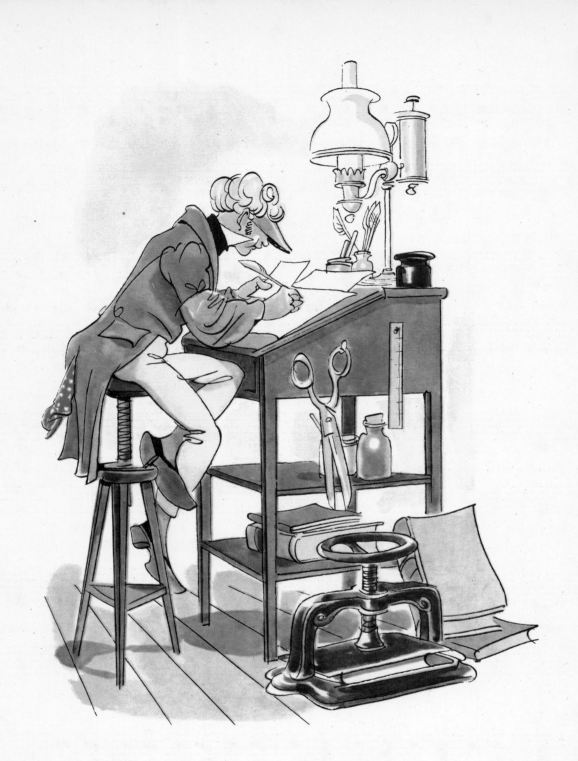

Sir Joseph paused for a moment amid the cheers that followed his singing. Proudly he stalked about the deck and adjusted his fine cocked hat. Then, settling his monocle, firmly, he looked at at his audience.

Yes, this was a good crew, an excellent crew, indeed. It might be well to tell the men how he had risen to the proud position of First Lord of the Admiralty.

To think that he, Sir Joseph Porter, K.C.B. had begun as a lowly office boy, cleaning windows, sweeping the floor, and polishing up the big front door handle. And he had polished it so carefully that he had been very well rewarded.

But that was only the beginning. Sir Joseph had gone on. After an office boy he arose to the proud position of clerk, wearing clean collars and a brand new suit as he carefully copied letters in a big round hand.

Higher and still higher he had climbed to the top. Yes, he would tell his life story, and who knew what might happen to the humble sailor lads before him?

He would end by telling all those who lived on the land that if they stayed close to their desks and never went to sea, that like him, they would one day be proud rulers of the Queen's Navee!

Clearing his throat delicately, he began his song.

When I Was a Lad

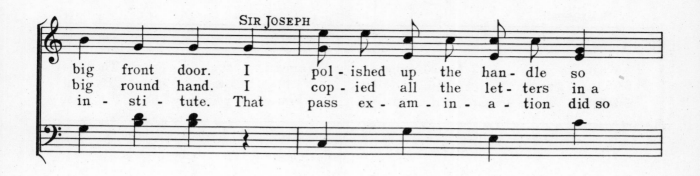

SIR JOSEPH

big   front   door.   I   pol - ished   up   the   han - dle   so
big   round   hand.   I   cop - ied   all   the   let - ters   in a
in - sti - tute.   That   pass ex - am - in - a - tion   did so

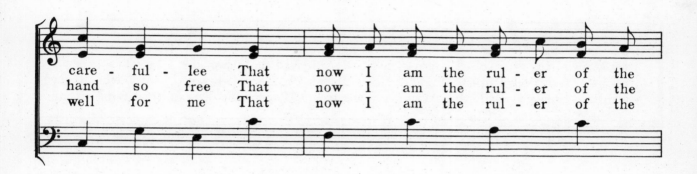

care - ful - lee   That   now   I   am   the   rul - er   of   the
hand   so   free   That   now   I   am   the   rul - er   of   the
well   for   me   That   now   I   am   the   rul - er   of   the

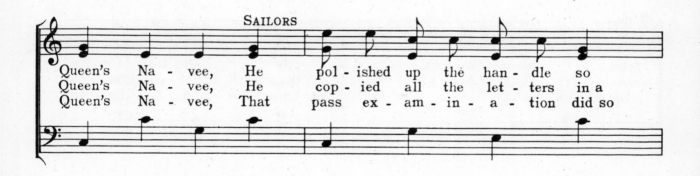

SAILORS

Queen's   Na - vee,   He   pol - ished   up   the   han - dle   so
Queen's   Na - vee,   He   cop - ied   all   the   let - ters   in a
Queen's   Na - vee,   That   pass ex - am - in - a - tion   did so

care - ful - lee,   That   now   he   is   the   rul - er   of   the   Queen's   Na - vee.
hand   so   free,   That   now   he   is   the   rul - er   of   the   Queen's   Na - vee.
well   for   he,   That   now   he   is   the   rul - er   of   the   Queen's   Na - vee.

SIR JOSEPH

4. Of le - gal knowl - edge I ac - quired such a grip That they
5. I grew so rich __ that __ I was __ sent By a
6. Now lands - men all, __ who __ ev - er you may be, If you

took me in - to a part - ner - ship, And that jun - ior part - ner -
pock - et bor - ough in - to Par - lia - ment. I __ al - ways vot - ed at my
want to rise to the top of the tree, If your soul is - n't fet - tered to an

ship, I ween, Was the on - - ly ship that I had
par - ty's call, And I nev - er thought of think - ing for my -
of - fice stool, Be __ care - ful to be guid - ed by this

SAILORS

ev - er seen, Was the on - - ly ship that he had
self at all. He __ nev - er thought of think - ing for him -
gold - en rule — Be __ care - ful to be guid - ed by this

36

ev - er seen. But that kind of ship so
self at all. I— thought so lit-tle, they re -
gold - en rule: Stick— close to your desks, and

suit - ed me, That now I am the rul - er of the
ward - ed me, By mak - ing me the rul - er of the
nev - er go to sea, And you all— may be rul - ers of the

Queen's Na - vee. But that kind of ship so
Queen's Na - vee. He— thought so lit-tle, they re -
Queen's Na - vee. Stick— close to your desks, and

suit - ed he, That now he is the rul - er of the Queen's Na - vee.
ward - ed he, By mak - ing him the rul - er of the Queen's Na - vee.
nev - er go to sea, And you all— may be rul - ers of the Queen's Na - vee.

37

With a flourish, Sir Joseph finished his long story, and surrounded by his flock of admiring, fluttering women, left for an inspection of the ship. At once the sailors broke ranks and, glad to be free at last, hurried off to their quarters.

"Sir Joseph is a true gentleman, courteous and kind to even the humblest tar," declared the boatswain.

"True," agreed Ralph Rackstraw, "but we are not the *very* humblest, for Sir Joseph tells us that a British seaman is any man's equal, excepting his!"

"Well spoke! Well spoke!" cried the sailors.

"Messmates," continued Ralph, "My mind's made up. I'll speak to our Captain's daughter now, and tell her like an honest man of the honest love I have for her."

"Aye! Aye!" shouted the merry crew of the PINAFORE.

"And here's news, lads," called the boatswain, taking a paper from his pocket. Look you now, a song that Sir Joseph, himself, made for us to sing, called, "A British Tar."

"That's us, maties!" cried the men. "Come, let's hear it."

One of the sailors, already reading the words, broke into a roar of mirth.

"This, me brawny boys, is what it says about us," he howled, reading aloud:

> 'His nose should pant and his lips should curl,
> His cheeks should flame and his brow should furl."

In a moment the deck was rocking with shouts of laughter as the song was sung by the crew.

A British Tar

1. A Brit - ish tar is a soar - ing soul, As
2. His eyes should flash with an in - born fire, His

free as a moun - tain bird; — His en - er - get - ic fist should be
brow with scorn be — wrung; He nev - er should bow down to a

read - y to re - sist A dic - ta - tor - ial
dom - i - neer - ing frown, Or the tang of a ty - rant

very fast

move. His nose should pant, and his lip should curl, His
tongue. His foot should stamp, and his throat should growl, His

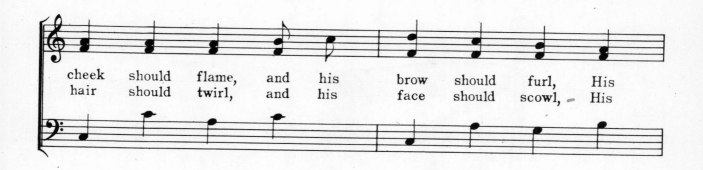

cheek should flame, and his brow should furl, His
hair should twirl, and his face should scowl, His

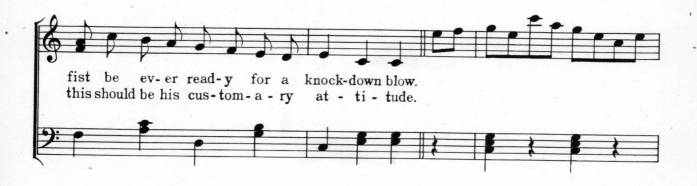

bo-som should heave, and his heart should glow, And his
eyes___ should flash, and his breast pro-trude, And___

fist be ev-er read-y for a knock-down blow.
this should be his cus-tom-a-ry at-ti-tude.

With howls of laughter, Sir Joseph's prize song was ended and the crew turned to listen to the joyous singing of Josephine and Ralph, now that he had won the hand of his fair lady. Quietly they gathered around the happy pair and in low tones, helped to plan their escape from the PINAFORE.

"Tonight, when all is quiet and darkness has settled over the ship, we'll steal ashore," they whispered eagerly.

Dick Deadeye, hiding in the hatchway, listened with all his might, and stealing up behind the plotting group, burst upon them harshly.

"Stop, you villains!" he cried. "Your plan will never be carried out. This proud woman is a lady, the daughter of your gallant Captain. And you, Ralph Rackstraw, are only a slave that crawls the water."

"Halt!" cried the crew, angrily. "No more of your taunts, Dick Deadeye!"

Not even this threat to the plans could stop the rejoicing of the crew, and rallying around the lovely Josephine, they toasted her gallantly in their rousing song: "Let's Give Three Cheers for the Sailor's Bride."

Dusk had began to gather on the deck of the PINAFORE, and quietly the members of the plotting group stole to their quarters to await nightfall and the hour of escape.

Let's Give Three Cheers

Let's give three cheers for the sail- or's bride, Who casts__ all thought of

rank a - side— And gives up home__ and for - tune, too, For the

hon - est love of a sail - or true! Tra, la, la, la, la, la,

la, la, la, la, la, la, la, la, la, la, la, la, la,

la, la, la, la, la, la, la, la, la, la, la, la, la, la, la,

la, la, la, la, la,   la, la, la, la, la,   la, la, la, la, la,

la,   la, la, la, la,   la, la, la, la, la,   la, la, la, la, la,

la, la, la, la, la,   la, la, la, la, la, la.   Let's give three cheers for the

sail - or's bride, Who   casts__ all   thoughts of   rank a - side, And

gives up home and for- tune, too, For the   hon - est love of a   sail - or true!

PART TWO

EVENING had settled over Portmouth Harbor, and a sprinkling of bobbing lights told of small craft resting from their labors of the long day. Over all, the full moon kept sharp watch, winking an eye at the scarred old man-o'-war, the PINAFORE, looming sharply from the lapping black water.

Her decks were quiet now, save for the strumming of a guitar, and Little Buttercup sat waiting below for the song of the Captain, which began anxiously enough:

"Fair moon, to thee I sing; bright regent of the heavens,
  Say, why is everything either at sixes or at sevens?"

The song ended with a sigh, and coming down the narrow stairs to the quarter deck, Captain Corcoran discovered the plump peddler woman, her basket empty at her side.

"Buttercup! You should have gone ashore, little one."

"Aye, sir, but you were troubled," answered kindly Mrs. Cripps, "and I would see you smile before I go."

"Smile? Ah no, Buttercup, — not with misfortunes tumbling round about me. My crew is beginning to rebel, my only daughter smiles on a lowly tar, and Sir Joseph is storming."

Out of the darkness, Buttercup rose suddenly to her feet.

"Captain, take care!" she cried mysteriously. "Your poor bumboat woman has gypsy blood in her veins. There is a change in store for you. Be prepared!"

In a low voice, Buttercup began her strange song, "Things are seldom what they seem."

Things are Seldom What they Seem

49

Though to catch your drift I'm striv-ing, It is sha-dy, it is

sha-dy; I don't see at what you're driv-ing, Mys-tic

BUTTERCUP

la-dy— mys-tic la-dy. Stern con-vic-tion's o'er_ him steal-ing

That the mys - tic la - dy's_ deal-ing In o-rac-u-

lar re-veal-ing. Yes, I know— that is so! *ff*

"Strange sayings, indeed," declared the Captain, watching Little Buttercup lovingly as she quickly disappeared, "And truly a timely warning."

No sooner had she gone than from the shadows strode Sir Joseph, his forehead wrinkled in an angry frown.

"Captain Corcoran, I am disappointed in your daughter," he declared hotly. "I have spoken to her without success, and so I do not think that she will do."

"Perhaps it is your high rank that dazzles her," suggested the Captain, soothingly. "But if you assured her of your rule that love has no rank, she might listen to your suit."

A ray of hope gleamed in the eyes of Sir Joseph.

"An excellent suggestion," he agreed heartily, "and I shall act upon it. But see, your daughter is here. I shall speak to her at once."

Josephine, startled at sight of the two men, began to move swiftly away.

"Pray, madam, do not go!" cried Sir Joseph, hastily. "I have just learned that you are dazzled by my high position. But you need not be, for true love levels all ranks."

A bright smile swept the face of the lovely Josephine.

"Then the high and the low may live happily together!" she cried joyfully, "Thank you for your kind words, sir."

There was instant rejoicing, and all three broke into merry dancing, singing as they skipped along: "Never mind the why or wherefore."

Never Mind the Why and Wherefore

CAPTAIN 1. Nev - er mind the why and where-fore, Love can
SIR JOSEPH 2. Nev - er mind the why and where-fore, Love can
JOSEPHINE 3. Nev - er mind the why and where-fore, Love can

lev - el ranks, and there - fore, Though his Lord-ship's sta - tion's
lev - el ranks, and there - fore, Though your nau - ti - cal re -
lev - el ranks, and there - fore, I ad - mit the jur - is -

might - y, Though stu - pen - dous be his brain, Though her
la - tion, In my set could scarce - ly pass, Though you
dic - tion, Ab - ly have you played your part, You have

tastes are mean and flight-y, And her for-tune poor __ and plain.
oc - cu - py a sta-tion In the low-er mid - dle class.
car-ried firm con - vic-tion To my hes-i-tat - ing heart.

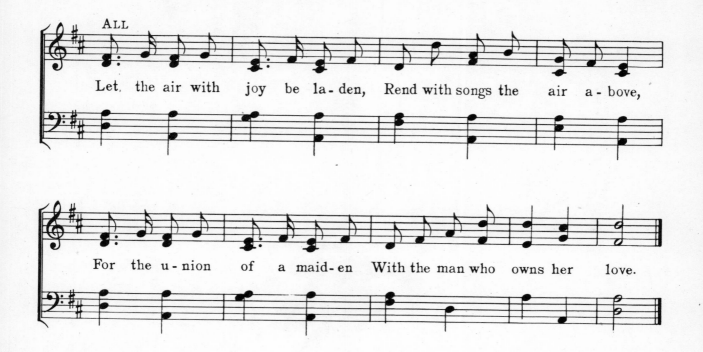

ALL

Let the air with joy be la-den, Rend with songs the air a-bove,

For the u-nion of a maid-en With the man who owns her love.

The night wind blew gently across the decks and Captain Corcoran looked happily after his beloved daughter as she danced gaily away to her cabin. From his merry tripping, Sir Joseph was weary, indeed, and took off his fine hat to wipe his brow.

"Ah, my good Admiral, I cannot express to you my delight at what your words have meant to my daughter," cried the Captain, his face beaming with contentment.

"And 'twas only my official statement that love levels all ranks," chuckled Sir Joseph, and wheeling on his heel, he prepared to take a turn about the ship.

Just as he disappeared, something near him moved in the shadows, and Captain Corcoran was instantly alert.

"Who goes there?" he demanded sternly.

Out of the darkness, the twisted form of a sailor ambled toward him, a smile of triumph on his ugly face.

"Captain!" whispered the tar, "its me. Its only Dick Deadeye."

"Deadeye! But what are you doing here?"

"Please don't shrink from me, sir," whimpered the sailor. "I'm not pleasant to look at, but I ain't as bad as I seem."

"Then what would you with me?" demanded the Captain, shortly. "Speak up, man!"

Looking around carefully to see that no one was listening, Deadeye crept closer.

"Captain," he whispered, "I've come to give you warning. Listen!" And in a rough voice the tar began his story.

Kind Captain, I've Important Information

The mer - ry, mer - ry maid - en, The mer - ry, mer - ry

maid - en, Sing hey, the mer - ry maid - en____ and the tar.

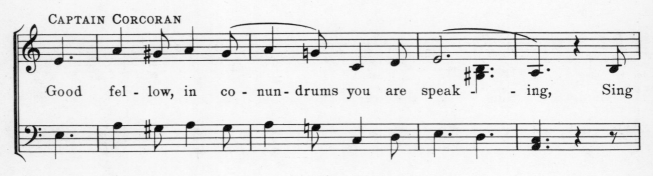

CAPTAIN CORCORAN

Good fel - low, in co - nun - drums you are speak - - ing, Sing

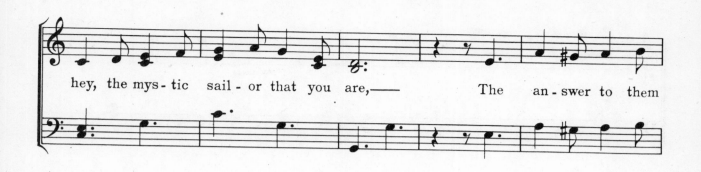

hey, the mys - tic sail - or that you are,——— The an - swer to them

vain - ly I am seek - ing, Sing hey, the mer - ry maid - en and the

tar,——— The mer - ry, mer - ry maid - en, The mer - ry, mer - ry

maid - en, Sing hey, the mer - ry maid - en——— and the tar.

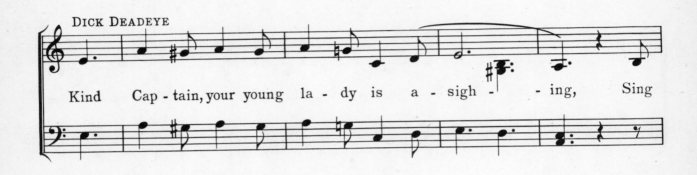

DICK DEADEYE

Kind Cap - tain, your young la - dy is a - sigh - - ing, Sing

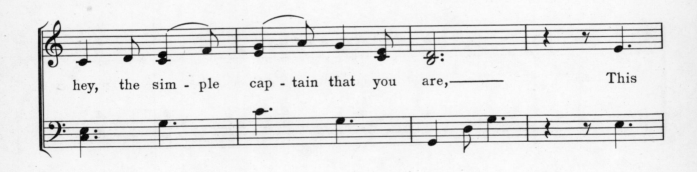

hey, the sim - ple cap - tain that you are, —— This

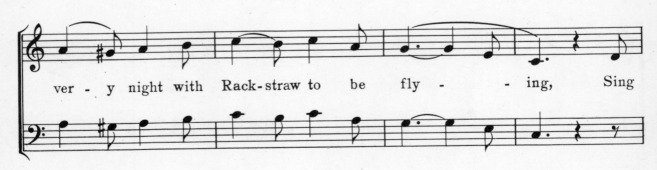

ver - y night with Rack-straw to be fly - - ing, Sing

64

hey, the mer - ry maid - en and the tar.———— The

mer - ry, mer - ry maid - en, The mer - ry, mer - ry maid - en, The

much too mer - ry maid - en ——— and the tar.

Good fel - low, you have giv - en time - ly warn - ing, Sing

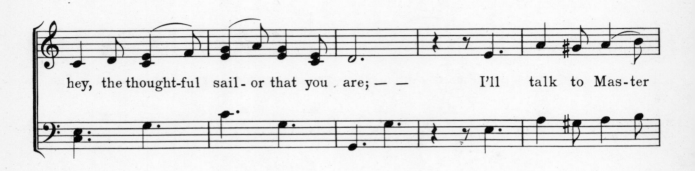

hey, the thought-ful sail - or that you are; — — I'll talk to Mas - ter

Rack-straw in the morn - ing, Sing hey, the cat - o' - nine tails and the

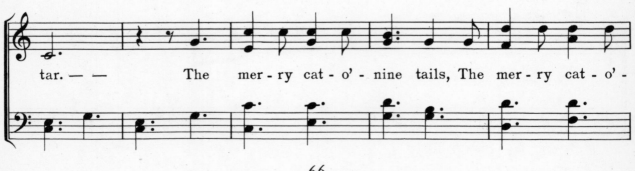

tar. — — The mer - ry cat - o' - nine tails, The mer - ry cat - o' -

nine - tails, The mer - ry cat - o' - nine - tails, — and the tar!

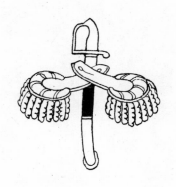

The Captain could not believe his ears at the horrible news brought to him by the tar, and drawing his cloak tightly about him, he anxiously paced the deck, stopping at last before the crouching sailor. In hushed tones he spoke so that none might hear.

"I thank you for your timely warning, Deadeye. But see to it that you speak to no one of your visit to me."

The evil smile spread more broadly over the twisted face of the tar as he shuffled back into the shadows, rubbing his hands together and muttering greedily:

"They are foiled, foiled, foiled!"

Down the long passageway there was a low creaking of a door opening, and from her darkened cabin, followed closely by Buttercup, Josephine crept along the deck to meet the crew, a small bundle clasped tightly in her hand.

As she drew nearer, she could hear the low voices of the sailors, still planning each step of the escape, chanting softly: "Carefully on tiptoe stealing," their song broken now and then by a sharp cracking noise.

"Goodness me! What was that?" cried someone in alarm.

"Silence!" came the sharp reply. "It was the cat!"

Now the time had come to leave the PINAFORE, and out of the darkness stole Josephine and Ralph, their hearts pounding for joy as they moved toward the side of the ship, Buttercup and the crew following close behind.

Carefully on Tiptoe Stealing

Care-ful-ly on tip-toe steal-ing, Breath-ing gen-tly as we may, Ev-'ry step with cau-tion feel-ing, We will soft-ly steal a-way. Good-ness me! Why what was that? Si-lent be, It was the cat!

SAILORS   CAPTAIN   SAILORS

It was, it was the cat! They're right, it was the cat! Pull a-

shore in fash - ion stead - y, Hy - men will de - fray the

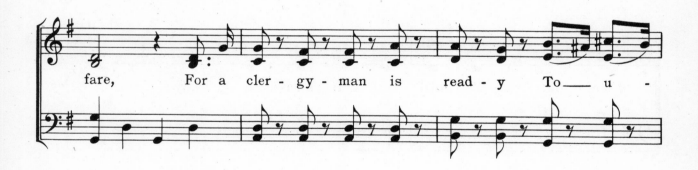

fare, For a cler - gy - man is read - y To___ u -

nite the hap - py pair! Good-ness me, Why, what was that?

71

DICK DEADEYE — SAILORS

Si - lent be,   A - gain the cat!   It   was   a - gain that

CAPTAIN — JOSEPHINE

cat! They're right,   it was the cat!   Ev -'ry step with cau - tion

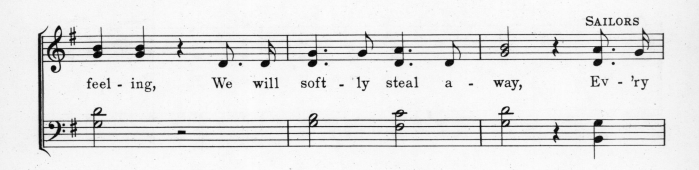

SAILORS

feel - ing,   We will soft - ly steal a - way,   Ev -'ry

step with cau - tion   feel - ing, We will steal a - way.

72

The sisters, cousins, and aunts of Sir Joseph, bursting with the excitement of the adventure, fluttered after the sailors, their eyes shining in the moon glow. Just as they reached the gangplank leading to shore, out stepped the Captain!

"Hold!" he cried, throwing back his long cape. "And now, my daughter, where could you be going with the crew at this hour of the night?"

There was not a sound to break the tense stillness.

"It is true that these men are excellent for routing any foe at sea," continued the Captain, "but as for accompanying my daughter, their low rank does not permit."

Instantly the crew was in rebellion.

"What is this?" they cried angrily, "if we can overcome the roughest enemy, then surely we may walk and talk with our Captain's daughter!"

From the group of surly tars, Ralph stepped quickly forward.

"Proud officer," said he, "Sir Joseph has led us to believe that we are any man's equal. And so I have dared to speak to your daughter, and have told her of the honest love in my heart for her."

Josephine moved quickly to Ralph's side.

"It is true, father," she cried, "that this sailor is humble, poor, and lowly born! But we must not forget that he is still an Englishman."

At once the challenging cry went up.

"An Englishman! He is an Englishman!"

He is an Englishman

For— he him-self has said— it, And it's great-ly to his cred - it That he is an Eng-lish - man, That he is an Eng-lish - man! For he might have been a Roo-sian A French, or Turk, or Proo-sian, Or per-haps I - tal - i - an, Or, per-haps I - tal - i - an! But in spite of all temp-ta - tions To be-

long to oth - er na - tions, He re - mains an Eng - lish -

man! He re - mains an__ Eng - - - - lish -

man! For, in spite of all temp - ta - tions, To be -

long to oth - er na - tions, He re - mains an Eng - lish -

man! He re - mains an__ Eng - - - - lish - man!

Captain Corcoran tried hard to hold back the anger that was rising steadily within him. Even though the young tar was an Englishman, a union with his daughter was unthinkable. In fiery tones he spoke to Ralph.

"I am sorry to discourage a humble foremast hand, but when such a one seeks the hand of my daughter, I forbid it, sir," cried the Captain. Then, becoming very angry, indeed, he shouted fiercely, "It's too bad! Yes, sir, I repeat it, sir — IT's TOO BAD!"

Fluttering nervously at this terrible outbreak, the sisters, cousins, and aunts cried out in distress.

"This is truly alarming! Pray, don't go near him!"

At this very moment, who should appear but Sir Joseph, himself, an angry light shining in his pale eyes. Pulling furiously on his curled moustaches, he faced the Captain.

"My pain and my distress at your hard words, you may clearly see," he remarked coldly.

Captain Corcoran tried in vain to explain.

"Please, my lord, you do not understand," he cried.

"There can be no excuse. Go at once to your cabin, sir!" commanded the Admiral in iron tones.

Without a word the Captain left the deck.

Now Sir Joseph, himself somewhat upset, took a turn down the passageway, his coat tails bobbing over his short legs and the feathers in his high cocked hat shaking angrily as he marched stiffly along.

In a moment he returned to the anxious group awaiting him.

"Now, my good people," he declared, adjusting his monocle carefully, "you know well the rule of the Admiralty: In the British navy there shall be no taunts."

With little echoing cries, his maidenly relatives agreed.

"'Tis true! No taunts in the navy!" they chorused, their beribboned heads nodding vigorously.

Sir Joseph bowed his approval and turned stiffly to Ralph.

"My fine fellow," he began pompously, "for you are a fine fellow, I can see — tell me what has happened here."

At attention, Ralph began his story.

"Please, your Honor, it was thus-wise. You see, I am only a top-man, a foremast hand."

"Ah, my good man, do not belittle it," interrupted Sir Joseph hastily, "Your position as top-man is a very high one, indeed."

"So it is, your Honor," Ralph went on quickly, "and love burns as brightly there as it does in any other part of the ship, and Josephine is the fairest bud that ever blossomed."

At his words, the crew agreed in rousing cheers.

"Aye! Aye! 'Tis true!" they called lustily.

But Sir Joseph was shocked and angry, indeed, at the mention of Josephine, the love of his own brave heart. He would teach this tar a lesson that he would not soon forget.

"Seize this insolent sailor!" he thundered, "and thrust

him into the dungeon!"

As two stalwart mariners hastened to do his bidding, binding Ralph fast, Josephine flung herself before the proud Admiral, weeping bitterly.

"Oh, Sir Joseph, spare him!" she cried, "for I love him dearly. Do not send him away, I pray you."

But the Admiral would not listen to her pleading.

"Off with him!" he shouted. "Off with him to the dungeon!"

Ralph was led quickly away, and as Josephine watched sorrowfully, her heart stirring song rang after him into the moonlit night:

    "Farewell, my own,
      Light of my life, farewell."

Farewell, My Own

Fare - well, my own, — — — — Light of my life, fare-well! — — — —

For crime un-known I .go to a dun - geon cell. — — — —

I will a - tone; — — — — In the mean-time, fare-well! — — — —

And all a - lone re-joice in your dun - geon cell! — — —

Little Buttercup, watching sadly from the shadowy darkness, could bear the sorrow of the heart broken Josephine no longer, and stepping forward suddenly, she called after the daughter of her beloved Captain.

"Wait, my pretty one! Do not mourn your loss too deeply, for the secret that I must now confess will set your beautiful heart rejoicing."

A secret to set all straight! A flutter of excitement swept over the deck as Buttercup began her story:

A Many Years Ago

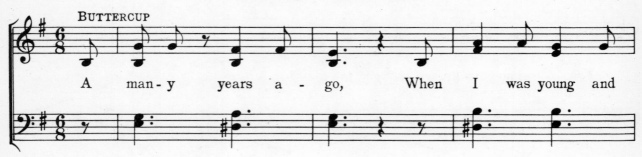

A man-y years a - go, When I was young and

charm-ing As some of you may know, I prac-tised ba - by

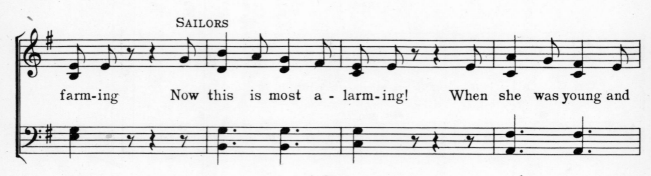

farm-ing Now this is most a - larm-ing! When she was young and

82

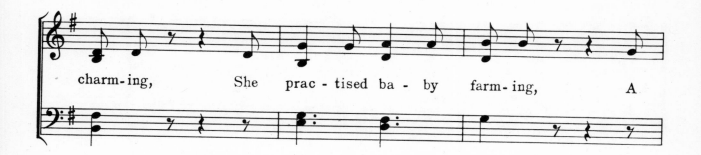

charm - ing, She prac - tised ba - by farm - ing,

A

BUTTERCUP

man - y years a - go. Two ten - der babes I nuss'd:

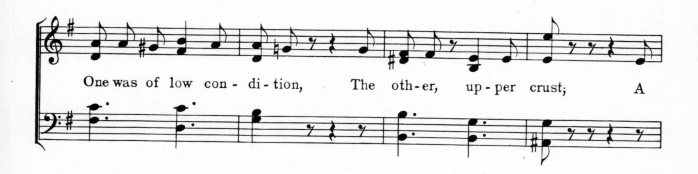

One was of low con - di - tion, The oth - er, up - per crust;

A

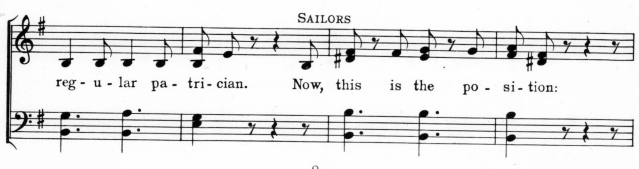

SAILORS

reg - u - lar pa - tri - cian. Now, this is the po - si - tion:

One was of low con - di - tion, The oth - er a pa - tri - cian, A

BUTTERCUP

man - y years a - go. Oh, bit - ter is my cup! How-

ev - er could I do it? I mixed those chil - dren up, And

SAILORS

not a crea - ture knew it! How - ev - er could you do it? Some

day, no doubt, you'll rue it, Al - though no crea - ture knew it, So

BUTTERCUP

man-y years a - go.   In time each lit - tle waif   For-

sook his fos-ter moth-er,   The well-born babe was Ralph—   Your

SAILORS

cap-tain was the oth-er!   They left their fos - ter moth-er   The

BUTTERCUP

one was Ralph, our broth-er,   Our cap-tain was the oth-er,   A

man-y years a - go.   *p*

85

Sir Joseph could not hide his astonishment at the news of the peddler woman.

"Then I am to understand that Captain Corcoran and Ralph were exchanged in childhood, and that Ralph is really the Captain, and the Captain is Ralph?" he questioned.

"Aye, your honor," responded Buttercup, happily, "that is true."

"Dear me! Dear me!" exclaimed Sir Joseph, pulling hard on his moustaches, "Let the two appear before me at once!"

Before many minutes had passed, Ralph strode smartly upon the deck of the Pinafore, more handsome than ever in fine captain's uniform, while behind him followed the Captain in simple sailor's clothing.

At sight of him, Josephine hastened to her beloved father with saddened cries.

"My own father — a common sailor!" she wept.

But Sir Joseph was highly pleased at the strange turn of events, and beaming happily, he approached the two men.

"Captain," said he to Ralph, "ask that fine seaman there, to step forward.

"Very well, sir," replied Ralph, "Corcoran, three paces to the front, march!"

The Captain obeyed at once, to stand silently at attention.

"Corcoran, you are an extremely fine fellow," remarked Sir Joseph, briskly.

"Yes, your Honor," returned the Captain, promptly.

"So all of these years that have passed, even from child-

86

hood until now, it seems that you were Ralph, and that Ralph was you."

"So it seems, your Honor," came the dutiful reply.

Sir Joseph stalked gleefully about the deck and returned to face the Captain.

"Then I need not tell you, sir, that now, after your change in rank, a marriage with your daughter could not possibly be."

"But, your Honor," pleaded the Captain, earnestly, "By your own words, love makes all ranks equal."

Sir Joseph smiled knowingly.

"Ah, my good fellow, you are quite right, indeed. That is true in all cases — excepting my own."

With mincing step, the gallant Admiral approached Josephine, and taking her hand, led her proudly to Ralph.

"Here, take her, sir," he commanded, "and mind you treat her kindly."

Cheers rose unchecked from the happy seamen.

"Hurrah! Hurrah! Hurrah!" they shouted.

And now, not one, but three happy pairs could live joyously ever after: The Captain and his Little Buttercup, Sir Joseph and his favorite cousin, Hebe, and Josephine and her captain, Ralph.

Cheering and singing, they danced about the decks of the old man-o'-war, their gay melodies ringing out merrily into the night as the moon smiled down on the happy company aboard Her Majesty's Ship, the PINAFORE.

I'm Called Little Buttercup*

I'm called Lit-tle But-ter-cup, dear Lit-tle But-ter-cup, Though I could nev-er tell why, — — But still I'm called But-ter-cup, poor Lit-tle But-ter-cup, Sweet Lit-tle But-ter-cup I, — — I've snuff and to-bac-cy and ex-cel-lent jack-y, I've scis-sors, and

*The melody of this song may be played in octaves.

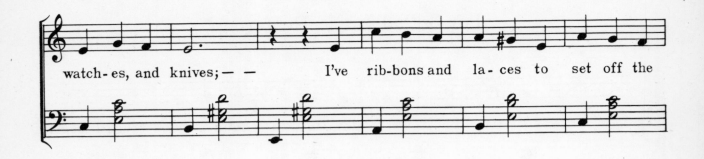

watch- es, and knives; — — I've rib-bons and la - ces to set off the

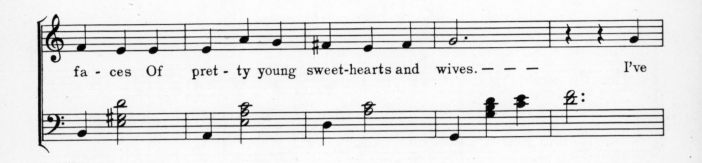

fa - ces Of pret - ty young sweet-hearts and wives. — — — I've

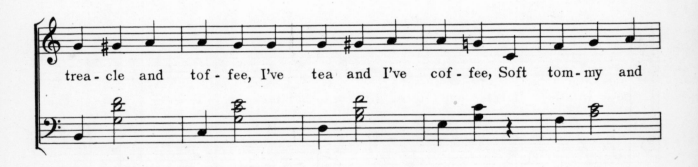

trea - cle and tof - fee, I've tea and I've cof - fee, Soft tom- my and

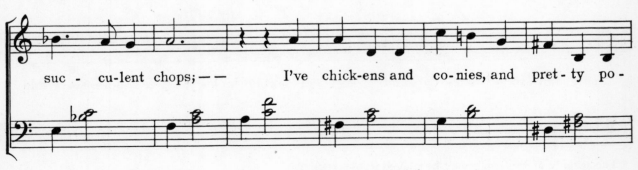

suc - cu-lent chops; — — I've chick-ens and co-nies, and pret - ty po-

lo - nies, And ex - cel - lent pep- per- mint drops, _____ Then

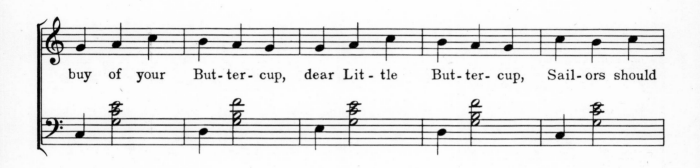

buy of your But- ter- cup, dear Lit - tle But- ter- cup, Sail- ors should

nev - er be shy; — — — So buy of your But- ter- cup,

poor Lit- tle But- ter- cup, Come, of your But- ter- cup, buy. _____

I Am the Captain of the Pinafore

CAPTAIN ... SAILORS

I am the cap-tain of the Pin-a-fore!—And a right good cap-tain,

CAPTAIN

too!——— You're ver-y, ver-y good, And be it un-der-stood, I com-

SAILORS

mand a— right good crew.——— We're ver-y, ver-y good, And

CAPTAIN

be it un-der-stood, He com-mands a— right good crew.——— Though re-

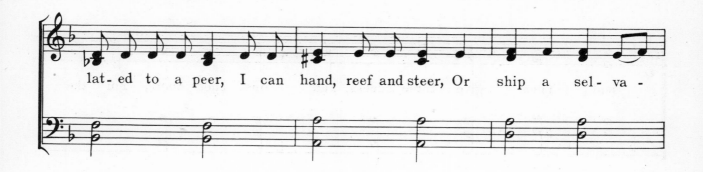

lat- ed to a peer, I can hand, reef and steer, Or ship a sel - va -

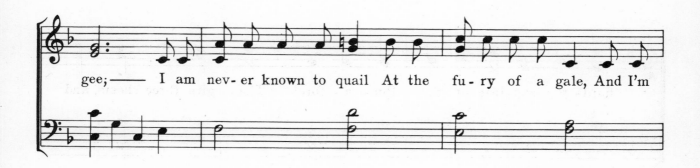

gee;—— I am nev- er known to quail At the fu - ry of a gale, And I'm

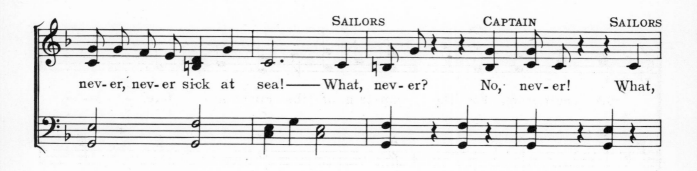

SAILORS   CAPTAIN   SAILORS

nev- er, nev- er sick at sea!——What, nev- er? No, nev- er! What,

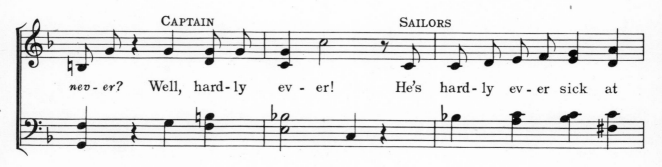

CAPTAIN   SAILORS

nev- er? Well, hard- ly ev - er! He's hard- ly ev - er sick at

93

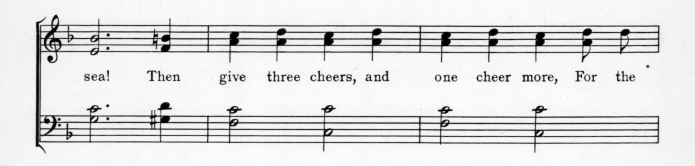

sea! Then give three cheers, and one cheer more, For the

hard - y cap-tain of the Pin - a - fore! Then give three cheers, and

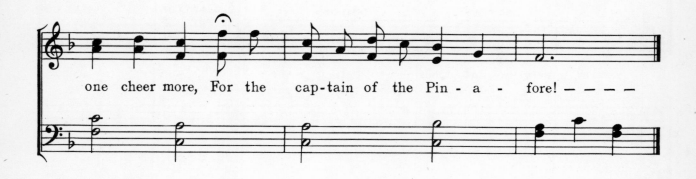

one cheer more, For the cap-tain of the Pin - a - fore! — — — —

He is an Englishman

For— he him-self has said— it, And it's great-ly to his

cred - it That he is an Eng-lish-man, That he

is an Eng-lish-man! For he might have been a Roo-sian A

French, or Turk, or Proo-sian, Or per-haps I-tal-i-an, Or, per-

haps I-tal-i-an! But in spite of all temp-ta-tions To be-

long to oth-er na-tions, He re-mains an Eng-lish-

man! He re-mains an___ Eng - - - - lish-

man! For, in spite of all temp-ta-tions, To be-

long to oth-er na-tions, He re-mains an Eng-lish-

man! He re-mains an___ Eng - - - - lish-man!